Mindful Healthcare

20 Exercises to Get "In the Zone" with Your Patients

Jennifer Llado, MS, MS, CCC-SLP

Dan Eisner, MS, OTR/L, CC

©Copyright, 2017, by Jennifer Llado and Dan Eisner
All rights reserved.
www.DanEisnerConsulting.com

Printed in the United States of America
ISBN: 978-0-9976757-1-9

TABLE OF CONTENTS

TABLE OF FIGURES

INTRODUCTION

For Therapists or other Healthcare Professionals:

The notion of *mindfulness* is becoming increasingly popular for good reason. It has been shown to offer profound physical, mental, and emotional healing benefits, all of which lead to improved personal and professional outcomes. Mindfulness is the foundation of being "in the zone," or the state of consciousness where we (and our patients) perform at our best.

For this reason, we have created 20 exercises to get you and your patients "in the zone" and ready to fully engage in treatment. These 5- to 10-minute exercises are based on the latest advances in neuroscience, energy medicine, and practical spirituality. They are incredibly simple, yet profoundly powerful. The following exercises are essentially mini-meditations that can significantly improve the quality of your treatment sessions by giving you and your patients immediate access to a peaceful state of mind, free from internal distractions.

A Note for Speech-Language Pathologists (SLPs): Meditation exercises that can be combined with speech, language, cognitive, and swallowing goals have been marked with a symbol (*) in front of the title. The Kirtan Kriya meditation (instructions on page 43) has been proven to result in positive cognitive changes for those with mild cognitive impairment (MCI). And in new research findings, the Double the Exhale meditation, on page 28, has potential benefits for individuals post stroke.

For Caregivers:

The stress of being a caregiver can take a toll on your emotional and physical health. This is not just a psychological or imaginary effect. It is a very real increase in levels of cortisol (the stress hormone). When you, as a caregiver, become overwhelmed with stress (a very natural occurrence), your ability to provide the most compassionate, effective care is likely to diminish.

Science has demonstrated that just 15 minutes a day of stress-relieving activity can significantly help prevent cortisol from reaching dangerous levels. The exercises in this book can be completed in short 5- to 10-minute increments and can easily be incorporated into your daily routines. In other words, you don't need to carve out extra time in your schedule for these simple practices.

It is unlikely that these exercises (or anything, for that matter) will ever completely get rid of the ongoing stress of being a caregiver. However, you will likely feel a great burden lifted as you practice these mini-meditations. In time, they will improve your ability to "tap into a peaceful state in the midst of the chaos of your everyday life" (Jill Bolte Taylor).

For Patients:

Dealing with change is stressful. As a person experiencing cognitive or physical changes, you naturally want your situation to be different. But obsessing about wanting things to be different (very easy to do) simply does not change what *is* and always results in increased stress. It also diminishes your ability to focus on the activities that will improve your overall health and well-being. Use these exercises as a tool to help improve your brain function and your ability to fully engage in treatment. The more time you spend in the zone, the faster you will be able to maximize your recovery.

BEFORE WE BEGIN

As discussed in *The Clinical Success Formula*, the importance of intention is at the heart of Mindful Healthcare, not to mention both personal and professional success. However, science has shown that approximately 95% of our thoughts and emotions are unconscious. This means that we are often not fully aware of our intentions, or what is driving our actions, in any given moment.

Consider the following: When you are rushing through traffic or just speeding mindlessly, what is your intention? Clearly your primary intention is to get to where you are going as fast as possible. You are making getting there more important than your own safety. While this may seem obvious, the reality is that the most important things in life (safety, being true to oneself, etc.) tend to become secondary.

It can be very easy to forget what matters the most (e.g., quality care; treating the person, *not* the patient; etc.) given the demands of our healthcare system. Stress from a variety of factors (and we know this from experience) can influence our intentions/approach to care, often in ways that are difficult to fully realize and accept. This leads to what we call "surface healthcare intentions."

Surface Healthcare Intentions

Common causes and examples of surface healthcare intentions include the following:

- When you're working with a difficult patient, you may be thinking/intending, "I just want to get this over with!"

- If you're the overachiever type, you may be thinking or intending, "I want to impress _____."
- When you're working with an unmotivated patient, you may be thinking/intending, "I need to fix him."

I'm not suggesting that these intentions are bad, but they do not point to what matters the most: simply doing the best we can independent of the circumstances. The bottom line is that we don't feel very good about ourselves when we forget to approach what we do with the best intentions, and instead seek immediate (e.g., "I want to this to be over.") or external gratification (e.g., "Look what I can do!", "I helped!"). These examples may seem obvious, but the subtle ways they can impact our approach to care are not always easy to see.

I'd like to invite you to think about your deepest intentions right now, and keep them in the forefront of your mind. Why did you choose a career in the healthcare field? What matters the most to you? Considering these questions is perhaps the first and most essential step to Mindful Healthcare that will naturally, in itself, improve the quality of care you provide, not to mention your own sense of fulfillment.

Here are a few examples of deeper intentions you may want to consider, or feel free to create your own list.

Deeper Healthcare Intentions

- My intention is to put forward my absolute best effort and trust that I will do well (i.e., not worry about the outcome).
- My intention is to treat each patient with the utmost compassion.
- My intention is to be the greatest role model I can be for the people I am serving.

- My intention is to approach each patient with acceptance, equality, and honesty.
- My intention is to impress myself by overcoming whatever challenges may arise.

Again, these are just examples. Your job is to choose intentions that deeply resonate within yourself. Paying close attention in this way is the best method to ensure your external success (impressing, helping, etc.), while fully enjoying your experiences and feeling great about yourself.

WHAT IS MINDFULNESS?

Mindfulness is a 2,600-year-old Buddhist tradition that is becoming increasingly popular for its various benefits to health and wellness. Mindfulness involves simply being aware of your thoughts with the goal of being fully in the present moment. For the purpose of this book, we are going to use *mindfulness* and *meditation* somewhat interchangeably. They are not exactly the same thing but they go hand-in-hand. *Meditation* is simply an umbrella term for various ways to get into the present moment. Mindfulness meditation is, in fact, one of the various techniques. With that said, do not get caught up in the definitions. As the old Zen saying goes, "If a finger is pointing at the moon, don't look at the finger."

As clinicians, you are most likely wondering how mindfulness and meditation can truly be used in your patient interactions. Where is the evidence-based practice? We have heard from many clinicians that feel uncomfortable using these tools. And, even if they are using them with patients, they want to keep it a secret, as though they are doing something wrong. Believe it or not, mindfulness is fully supported by over 3,000 peer-reviewed articles. Thus, understanding the science behind mindfulness can facilitate the process of letting go and tuning into what the idea of mindfulness meditation is pointing to: the energy or space in which all things exist.

In his book *You are the Placebo*, Dr. Joe Dispenza explains that everything physical is made of atoms. Yet atoms are 99.999% empty space, or energy. So, if we are not paying attention to the space behind everything that exists, we are literally missing out on 99.999% of reality.

As an analogy, think of the greater part of our identity as a huge open sky. The clouds in the sky represent "things" (mental ideas, images, our to-do lists, and, most importantly, our thoughts and emotions). Many of us become so consumed by our "clouds" (especially the thoughts and emotions) that we literally forget about the open sky, or the greater part of our identity. In difficult times, this is why we often say, "I need space." What we are truly saying is, "I am too caught up in my thoughts and emotions right now, and I need to get back in touch with me."

So there is nothing mystical or "woo-woo" about mindfulness meditation—it simply refers to the practice of being aware of the space (e.g., the sky, or your true self) while noticing the thoughts and emotions arising (e.g., the clouds).

Surely most people would agree that they think too much and are generally aware of the content (often negative) playing in their minds. However, we are frequently not aware of more subtle patterns of thought that judge, manipulate, and try to control our internal experiences. Critical thinking is an essential component to providing high-quality healthcare, so we are in no way advocating that we need to mute our thoughts. On the contrary, we are suggesting that mindfulness is a simple way of accessing a greater level of clarity, creativity, and innovation on a regular basis. Those moments of *really* seeing a beautiful sunset, a flower, or witnessing a true act of kindness become more meaningful. They are mini-breaks from the internal chaos that exists the majority of time.

And the good news is that we can cultivate these moments and learn to make them a natural part of our lives by practicing the simple yet powerful exercises outlined in this book. You will also quickly learn how to come up with your own. Truly, there are infinite ways to tap into the space or energy behind our thinking brain, all of which will improve the quality of our ability to heal.

The book *The Open-Focus Brain* by Dr. Les Fehmi and Jim Robbins essentially illustrates that narrow-focused attention (e.g., zooming in on the clouds) creates incoherence in the brain, whereas tapping into the space/sky (while noticing the clouds) facilitates coherent brain activity. Simply stated, when we are in the zone, we are paying attention to the cloud (e.g., a patient) *and* the sky (i.e., field of energy) at the same time.

Again, this is a state of consciousness we can learn to access. While we do not need brain scans to show that something different (and awesome!) is happening in the brain when we are in the zone, understanding a bit more of the science can help justify why we all can benefit from practicing these techniques on a regular basis.

THE SCIENCE OF MEDITATION

Peer-reviewed articles have found meditation to benefit the brain, the body, and our state of well-being in many ways. Table 1 is a simple visual outlining these benefits.

Table 1. Meditation's Effects on Brain, Body, and Mental State

BRAIN / COGNITION	BODY	MENTAL STATE
Increases cortical thickness	Decreases blood pressure	Decreases stress
Decreases activity in amygdala	Decreases heart rate	Decreases anxiety
Increases gray matter	Decreases cortisol	Decreases depression
Increases cerebral blood flow	Decreases pain	Decreases symptoms of panic disorder
Increases gyrification	Improves pain tolerance	Helps manage ADHD
Increases gamma brain waves	Reduces need for sleep	Helps manage stress
Increases sustained attention	Improves immune system	Improves empathy and positive relationships
Improves decision making	Reduces risk of heart disease and stroke	Reduces social isolation
Improves selective attention	Decreases inflammatory disorders	Increases feelings of compassion
Improves learning	Decreases cellular inflammation	Decreases loneliness

Improves memory	Prevents asthma	Reduces emotional eating
Improves self-awareness	Prevents inflammatory bowel disease	Reduces substance abuse in children
Improves visuospatial skills	Prevents rheumatoid arthritis	Reduces reactivity in children
Fosters creativity	Treats PMS symptoms	Increases self-esteem in children

Spiritual leader and physician Dr. Deepak Chopra proclaims that the mind and body are inseparably one. "Neurotransmitters like dopamine, oxytocin, serotonin, and opiates are both the molecules of emotions and immunomodulators that adjust our biological responses" (Chopra, 2010). Thus, emotions create physiological symptoms.

Chopra goes on to say, "There is no mental event that does not have a neural correlate. And there is no neural correlate that doesn't have a biological correlate." This phenomenon may contribute to the reason for two patients with similar diagnoses having two completely different outcomes. Therefore, medicine is beginning to look to the mind for answers to physical healing.

How Mindfulness Affects the Brain

Meditation is derived from the Latin words *meditari* (to exercise the mind) and *mederi* (to heal). This combination is made clear by several studies that have shown actual physical changes in the brain by using mindfulness tools. A study from Massachusetts General Hospital noted that after 8 weeks of mindful meditation the brains of these participants showed the following changes: (1) decreased activity in the amygdala, suggesting improved emotional stability; and (2) increased gray-matter density in the hippocampus, the center for learning and memory, and in structures associated with self-awareness, compassion, and introspection (Hölzel et al., 2011).

In 2013, a study assessed the effects of Mindfulness Based Stress Reduction (MBSR) on individuals with mild cognitive impairment (MCI). The MBSR group had increased functional connectivity between the posterior cingulate cortex and bilateral medial prefrontal cortex and left hippocampus compared to controls. In addition, MBSR participants had trends of less bilateral hippocampal volume atrophy than controls, indicating a potential positive impact on the regions of the brain related to MCI and Alzheimer's disease.

Newberg, Wintering, Khalsa, Roggenkamp, & Waldman (2010) compared cerebral blood flow (CBF) single-photon emission computed tomography (SPECT) imaging of advanced meditators and non-meditators. The CBF of meditators was significantly higher compared to non-meditators in the prefrontal cortex, parietal cortex, thalamus, putamen, caudate, and midbrain. The observed changes associated with long-term meditation appeared in structures of the attention network and also those related to emotion and autonomic function. Similarly, Luders et al. (2012) found correlation between years of meditation and gyrification in the brain.

While physical changes in the brain appear to be promising, clinicians require evidence that these brain transformations actually improve patient outcomes in order to determine the usefulness of meditation in their sessions.

How Mindfulness Affects Cognitive Function

Meditation not only creates a better-looking brain but also has been shown to increase cognitive functioning. Alexander, Langer, Newman, Chandler, & Davies were the first to identify this phenomenon in 1989. The study grouped 73 geriatrics into 3 groups: mindfulness, relaxation, and transcendental meditation (TM). The researchers assessed cognitive flexibility, verbal fluency, and memory immediately following the practice, again after 18 months, and finally, after 3 years. Amazingly, after 3 years, the TM group and the mindfulness group maintained 100% and 88% of their cognitive performance respectively while the relaxation group had lower scores.

Prakash et al. (2012) also looked at meditation's effect on the geriatric population. The study compared the cognitive skills of long-term meditators (10 years-plus) to non-meditating seniors. The results showed that the meditators performed better on tests of attention, speed of processing, ability to attention shift, and on tests using distracting factors.

Tai Chi is a form of meditation combined with slow, low-intensity movements. Mortimer et al. (2012) investigated the cognitive performance of geriatrics participating in Tai Chi three times a week. After 8 weeks, participants in the experimental group showed not only increased brain volume but also demonstrated statistically significant improvements in memory and thinking skills. Control group participants who participated in no activity showed brain shrinkage.

Positive changes in cognition do not necessarily require 8 weeks of training. Zeidan, Johnson, Diamond, David, & Goolkasian (2010) found improvement in cognitive performance after only a few brief sessions. Zeidan and colleagues' participants completed four 20-minute sessions of meditation training, resulting in significant improvements in visuospatial processing, working memory, and executive functions. But can we achieve positive results in cognitive performance in those individuals with disordered cognitive-linguistic abilities?

A study investigated the results of a Kirtan Kriya meditation program performed for 12 minutes daily in adults ages 52–70 with MCI or memory difficulties compared to participants in a music group. After 8 weeks, the meditation group demonstrated statistically significant improvements in verbal fluency compared to the music group (Newberg et al., 2010).

The benefits of meditation include increased cognitive performance as well as decreased stress, pain, anxiety, and mood. However, the reality is that these benefits are all entangled. Researchers believe that high levels of stress hormones may damage or shrink the hippocampus. A study by Rush University noted that stress-prone individuals with normal cognition were 40% more likely to develop MCI (Wilson et al., 2007). Furthermore, a meta-analysis of 41 cohort studies showed an annual conversion rate of up to 10% of those with MCI developing dementia over a 10-year span (Mitchell & Shiri-Feshki, 2009).

Healthcare providers have a primary role in identifying those with MCI and educating those who are at risk for dementia. Therefore, training our patients to practice stress-reducing exercises, such as meditation, is an essential preventative measure in combating dementia, maintaining optimal cognitive well-being, and even treating cognitive impairment.

Table 2. Studies Involving Mindfulness

RESEARCH ARTICLE	TYPE OF MINDFULNESS	PARTICIPANTS	AREA OF COGNITIVE IMPROVEMENT
Alexander et al. (1989)	Transcendental Meditation	Geriatric	Memory, Attention, Executive Functions, Language
Innes (2012)	Kirtan Kriya	Alzheimer's disease, Caregivers	Memory
Prakash et al. (2012)	Meditation	Geriatric	Attention
Newberg et al. (2010a)	Kirtan Kriya	Alzheimer's disease, Elderly, MCI	Memory, Language
Marshall et al. (2014 & 2015)	Unilateral Nostril Breathing	Stroke	Language
Pagnoni & Cekic (2007)	Zen	Geriatric	Attention
Van Leeuwen (2009)	Mindful Meditation	Geriatric	Attention

Chart adapted from Marciniak et al. (2014), *Frontiers in Behavioral Neuroscience*

Flowing vs. Stuck

We all know what it feels like to be "flowing." But have you ever really stopped to consider what that means? Think of the brain and body as an energetic hose. When we feel stuck, we have essentially created a "kink in the hose" by obsessing or trying to control our thoughts. When we are flowing, we are allowing our emotions or energy to come and go naturally, like passing storms.

Mindfulness meditation (simply being aware of the space and thoughts at the same time) is like "flow training camp," improving our ability to access the wonderful state of "flow" on a more regular basis.

Mindfulness Meditation is *Not* Just About Sitting Around Doing Nothing

Meditation is really a process of contemplation, self-reflection, and observation. It is a practice of learning how to pay attention, being aware without judgment, and staying in the zone. Formal meditation (e.g., eyes closed/focus on breath) is helpful, but it is equally, if not more, important to be mindful throughout the entire day.

Think of meditation as a process of becoming more self-aware, as opposed to just quieting the thinking mind. As we attend more closely to the space or energy from which our thoughts arise, the stressful internal dialogue that limits performance tends to diminish.

The exercises included here are not formal meditations, but they are profoundly effective in facilitating the process of tapping into the space/energy and essentially getting in the zone with your patients. You can find infinite gateways for accessing the present moment, decreasing stress, and maximizing potential. It's up to you to determine what options work best for you, both personally and professionally.

Consider these exercises as simply a helpful guide to get you started on your own journey.

Can I really start my patient interactions this way?

The intention of these exercises is simple. We want to be more present or in the zone with our patients. What could possibly be more important? Reaching and staying in the zone is a skill that requires training, especially given the incredibly fast-paced society in which we live.

Mindfulness meditation has profound emotional and physical benefits, not to mention helping to improve our ability to perform at our best. As previously mentioned, there is a plethora of research supporting the use of meditation. Table 2 notes how meditation is helpful in improving many cognitive skills including attention, language, and executive functioning. But that's not all. Meditation is an evidenced-based practice for improving physical, mental, and emotional health. Why is something so simple and free of cost not an essential component in our healthcare system? With your help, we hope to change that.

MEDITATION THROUGH THE SENSES

*FEELING "I"

<u>Time:</u> 5 min

Background

"I" is the most misused word in the English language (Tolle, *The Power of Now*). It is often used to reinforce identification with emotion. As an example, you might say, "I am stressed," which only creates more stress. This exercise will help you connect to the greater, energetic part of your identity.

Intention

To connect the word "I" to the *feeling* of who you are, which interrupts thought processes that create ongoing stress

Instructions

Turn your palms up*, close your eyes, and *feel* your hands.

If you are having trouble doing this, ask yourself:

How do you know your hands are there without looking at them?

Can you *feel* them?

Once you can *feel* your energy, slowly repeat the following alternating phrases for 3–5 minutes, as you stay connected to the feeling/energy in your hands:

"I am this feeling . . . this feeling is me . . . I am this feeling . . . this feeling is me . . ."

*<u>Note</u>: Placing the palms face up is a neurological trigger for relaxation.

*CALMING THROUGH THE SENSES

Time: 5 min

Background

Science has shown that excessive thinking creates ongoing stress. We often get trapped in negative patterns of thoughts (I'll never get better.) and emotions (sadness, anger, frustration) that make focusing on improving the situation nearly impossible. "You can't think and sense at the same time," (J. Dispenza, Advanced Workshop, May 2015) so focusing on what we notice with our senses is a great way to silence negative thoughts, which naturally results in being more relaxed.

Intention

To naturally calm the mind by paying attention to the senses, which interrupts the thought processes that perpetuate stress

Instructions

Begin by scanning through your senses.

Identify and label whatever you notice.

While there is no right or wrong way to do this, focusing on more subtle sensations tends to be more calming.

Example: I can feel the wind of my breath in my throat. I can hear the street noise. I can feel the weight of my body on the chair. I can smell the food trays.

Working with a patient or loved one—You can alternate back and forth verbalizing these sensations.

FEELING THE SPACE BETWEEN SOUNDS

Time: 5 min

Background

Focusing on the silence or "space" between words has been scientifically shown to produce alpha brain waves. These waves are associated with relaxation. The expression "I need space" is wise and common for this reason: space literally calms the busy mind that creates stress.

Intention

To create "the space" that reduces stress and induces calm and focused attention

Instructions

Slowly repeat the phrase below, pausing for 5 seconds between each word, with the intention of tuning into the silence or "space" between each word. It may feel a little strange. You will notice your mind wanting to race ahead. Remember that whatever happens is OK. Just do the best you can.

"I . . . (space) . . . am . . . (space) . . . this . . . (space) . . . calm . . . (space) . . . feeling."

*MOVING WITH INTENTION

Time: 5 min

Background

"It's the journey, not the destination, that really matters." We tend to be so focused on "getting there" that we often miss experiencing the treasures (i.e., sensations, insights, and lessons) along the way. Learning to move consciously (i.e., paying attention) reduces the internal chatter that causes stress while opening up to "the little things" that truly make the most difference.

Intention

To facilitate consciousness through movement

Instructions

Normally, we move without paying attention. This lack of consciousness prevents us from noticing the little things that can be very calming. Take a walk or ride around the room and see what you notice with your senses.

While there is no right or wrong way to do this, focusing on the subtle sensations tends to be most calming. You can practice verbalizing them out loud or just identifying them in your mind. You can also try just feeling them in your body without mentally labeling them (which is even more calming).

Example: I can hear the sound of our footsteps. I can hear the squeaking of the wheels. I can feel the wind on my arms. I can hear my breath.

Working with a patient or loved one—You can alternate verbalizing your experience as you walk. Or you can remain silent and share at the end of your little journey.

MEDITATION THROUGH BREATHWORK

*DOUBLE THE EXHALE

Time: 5 min

Background

Rapid and shallow breathing is a clear indication that the body has moved into a "fight or flight" survival state, occurring naturally when the body believes it is in physical danger. This stress response from the sympathetic nervous system is reinforced through improper breathing practices. "Double the Exhale" turns on the parasympathetic nervous system, causing the body to relax into the present moment. The inhale is about control (fight/flight), while the exhale is about letting go (relaxation).

Intention

To turn on the body's natural relaxation response by consciously activating the parasympathetic nervous system

Instructions

Breathe in to a count of 4, and then exhale to a count of 8.

It may feel strange at first because you have likely conditioned your body to take shallow breaths. We tend to take a lot of air in and do not fully breathe out. You would be doing the same thing if you were literally running from danger. Yet when we take a long exhale, our body begins to understand that we are not in danger. By doing this, we consciously override the stress response. You may have to consciously "force" the exhale, at first, in order to break the habitual cycle. However, if this is too uncomfortable the inhale-exhale ratio can be reduced (2:4 or 3:6).

<u>Working with a patient or loved one</u>—It can be helpful to count for them and to provide verbal cues as needed (especially to "keep exhaling" when necessary).

Breathe in . . . 1 . . . 2 . . . 3 . . . 4 . . . Breathe out . . . 1 . . . 2 . . . 3 . . . 4 . . . 5 . . . 6 . . . 7 . . . 8

<u>For Individuals Post Stroke</u>—New research suggests breathing through only one nostril increases brain activity in the opposite side of the brain. We can facilitate brain activity to the damaged hemisphere using the following guidelines:

LEFT BRAIN STROKE: Close off left nostril and breath only through right nostril.

RIGHT BRAIN STROKE: Close off right nostril and breath only through left nostril.

After 10 weeks of this breathing exercise, statistically significant improvements were noted in attention, language, anxiety, and depression (Marshall, Basilakos, Williams, & Love-Myers, 2014).

Try this exercise yourself while breathing out of one nostril.

FEELING THE WIND

Time: 5 min

Background

People often say, "I've tried deep breathing, and it doesn't work for me." Here is why: It does not work when we are distracted by the busy thinking mind (i.e., When is this going to make me feel better? Am I doing it right?). In order for deep breathing to be effective, one must actually be "with" the breath. Tuning in to the sensations of the breath is a great way to enter the present moment.

Intention

To calm the mind by introducing the powerful nature of conscious breathing

Instructions

Focus on the sensations of the "wind" going in and out of your body as you breathe consciously for 5 minutes. While there is no right or wrong way to do this, paying close attention to the air passing through the throat and the nose tends to be very effective.

Working with a patient or loved one—Guiding questions include the following:

Can I feel the wind in my throat?

Can I hear the air passing through my nostrils?

Can I feel the gentle wind of my breath on my hands?

HEART-CENTERED BREATHING

Time: 5 min

Background

The scientists at HeartMath, Inc. have shown that stress causes the heart to function in an erratic and incoherent state. This directly influences brain function by creating brain waves that are equally chaotic. However, they show that we can facilitate healthy heart and brain function simply by practicing heart-centered breathing. The following exercise was adopted from HeartMath's Quick Coherence® Technique. Exploring the resources available at www. heartmath.com is highly recommended.

Intention

To induce relaxation and healing by facilitating heart and brain wave coherence through heart-centered breathing

Instructions

Close your eyes and place your left hand on your heart. Imagine that you are breathing in and out of your heart.

Do your best to focus only on the sensation of your breathing with the intention of creating a neutral emotional state. Once you are feeling neutral, continue focusing on breathing in and out of your heart while thinking about a person, place, or thing that you love.

Then, remove the object of your attention and focus only on the *feeling* you get from that person, place, or thing. As you continue to breathe in and out of your heart, notice that the *feeling* you are experiencing from the object of your attention is in *you*. Continue to breathe, and remember that the feeling you are now experiencing represents who you are at your core.

INHALE "I," EXHALE "AM"

Time: 5 min

Background

"I" is the most misused word in the English language, as it often reinforces identification with roles of behavior (i.e., "I am a therapist." or "I am a patient."). We are not our roles of behavior, but rather the consciousness that chooses who we want to be (i.e., I want to be a therapist, a mom, a golfer). Learning to say "I am" and then listening to and feeling the silence that follows is a powerful tool for reducing stress and tuning into our true identity.

Intention

To quiet the mind and introduce the empowering nature of identifying with "I Am"

Instructions

Simply inhale thinking "I" and exhale thinking "Am."

Pause for a few seconds between each cycle while paying attention to the silent feeling or sensation that follows the word "Am."

Working with a patient or loved one—You can guide them by repeating the following:
"Inhale thinking 'I'... exhale thinking 'Am'... (pause)... feel the silence... Inhale thinking 'I'... exhale thinking 'Am'..."

As your patient naturally begins to relax and pick up the process independently, you may slow down or stop providing instruction (trust and go with your gut).

MEDITATION THROUGH ACTIVITY

WASHING HANDS

Time: 2 min

Background

While structured meditation is wonderful, bringing mindful attention to daily activities can be even more beneficial. Your brain is constantly rewiring itself, so practicing mindfulness during routine actions will slowly enhance your ability to reach a state of presence quickly and easily. Through this exercise, eventually your brain will automatically link mindfulness to hand washing. When this occurs, you will be in a state of peace and enjoyment more of the time.

Intention

To link mindfulness to routine activities to enhance clarity and peace throughout the day

Instructions

Place your hands under running water. Bring awareness to your hands. Then, expand your awareness to your senses. Notice the temperature of the water. Feel the water stream over your skin. Apply soap and notice the texture, smell, and sensation while slowly scrubbing your hands. Then, expand your awareness further to your body and your breath while rinsing your hands clean. Slowly wipe your hands dry while maintaining awareness to your physical body, your senses, and your entire energy field.

Note: Isn't it amazing that we have washed our hands thousands of times in the past but we were not even *there* in the present moment?

WRITING EXERCISE

Time: 5 min

Background

Sloppy handwriting can be a clear sign of just how fast we move through life. Instead of being conscious with each line or letter, we are racing to get the word finished. This leads to unnecessary stress. It also can be an unconscious strategy for feeling worse about ourselves. (My handwriting is messy = I am messy.) Learning to slow our pace and write one line or letter at a time is a great way to train the mind and body to stay focused in the moment.

Intention

To induce relaxation and improved task performance through conscious handwriting

Instructions

Write the following sentence in slow motion, paying close attention to each individual line of each letter. You can also focus in on your senses, such as the feel of the pencil, the sound of the pencil moving, and the pressure of the pencil on the paper. There is no right or wrong way to do this. It is simply about slowing down into the present moment, which will help you to relax and to write more neatly.

Example: I am slowing down and relaxing into the present moment.

*EATING AND DRINKING

Time: The length of a drink, meal, or snack

Background

Many of us eat unconsciously and often when we aren't even hungry. This is a learned and unconscious behavior that, similar to a drug, quiets the internal dialogue, providing a temporary feeling of relief. Eating and drinking consciously provides us with an opportunity to choose what and how much we are going to take in by listening to what our body really needs.

Intention

To tune into what our body needs and experience food and drink completely by consciously putting our attention to each sense

Instructions

1. Begin by *choosing* your food instead of it choosing you. Ask yourself, "Will this food further my healing and well-being?"
2. Before you start eating, use your senses. Notice the color, texture, and consistency. Smell the aroma.
3. When you are ready, begin eating or drinking slowly and deliberately.
4. Notice the texture and temperature, and taste each and every flavor.
5. Be aware of how the rest of your body feels.
6. Begin to notice when you become full or your thirst is quenched.
7. Be *present* throughout.

For therapists working with dysphagia patients—"Mindful swallowing" can decrease the anxiety and stress related to swallowing and improve the use of other strategies. Encourage your patients to visualize where the food and drink should go with each swallow.

WALKING WITH PRESENCE

Time: 1–10 min

Background

When combining mindfulness and movement, the *experience* becomes the meditation. During physical therapy and occupational therapy, the focus is often on a desired outcome (i.e., walk 150 feet). Whenever we are racing to a future outcome, we are *not* in the present moment. We also neglect feelings and sensations of the present moment that may be crucial pieces of information to improve healing and function.

Intention

To let go of future needs and remain present while engaging in physical activity

Instructions

Gaze forward and down, but do not look at anything in particular. Begin walking while placing your focus on each individual step. Notice the way your foot hits the floor, how your muscles feel, how you are holding your posture, and how you are breathing. Try not to make judgments about the thoughts and sensations coming through.

VERBAL MEDITATION

*I LOVE

Time: 5 min

Background

In the book *Love for No Reason*, author Marci Shimoff explains that love is really who we are and that our job in life is to expand in love. Yet part of human nature is to focus on our stress. In doing this, we tax our immune system, drain our energy resources, and dramatically slow the healing process. Focusing on what we love, on the other hand, releases oxytocin, which is very much a feel-good chemical. It also has been scientifically shown to turn on new genes for healing.

Intention

To boost the immune system through a release of oxytocin by focusing on love

Instructions

Close your eyes and consciously think about or verbalize things that you love. It can be anything at all, big or small. By contemplating things that elicit positive emotions, you release a hormone that promotes relaxation, trust, and emotional stability.

Example: I love petting friendly dogs . . . I love sunsets . . . I love lying in the grass . . . I love my nephew's smile.

Working with a patient or loved one—Alternating sharing out loud is a great practice. You may also sit silently, completing the activity internally, and then take a few minutes to share once the meditation is complete.

*I AM GRATEFUL FOR . . .

<u>Time:</u> 5 min

Background

In the state of gratitude, the body, mind, and soul are connected. And the subconscious mind, which harbors the negative internal dialogue, literally cannot be activated (J. Dispenza, Progressive Workshop, March 2013). Consciously practicing gratitude naturally raises our energy, improves emotional wellness, and frees up energy required for healing and homeostasis.

Intention

To boost the immune system and induce a relaxed state by consciously practicing gratitude

Instructions

Close your eyes and consciously think about things you are grateful for. You can also say them out loud. While there is no right or wrong way to do this, choosing what you are feeling grateful for in the particular moment is important, no matter how big or small.

<u>Example:</u> I am so grateful for my mom . . . I am so grateful that I have health insurance . . . I am so grateful for music . . . I am so grateful for my dog.

<u>Working with a patient or loved one</u>—Alternating sharing out loud is a great practice. You may also sit silently to complete this activity internally and then take a few minutes to share once the meditation is complete.

I AM . . .

Time: 5–15 min

Background

"So hum" is a yoga mantra. *So* means "I am" and *hum* means "that." Repeating "I am that" allows one to settle into his or her true self. When we say things like I'm tired, I'm lazy, or I'm sad, we are operating from a program in the brain that tricks us into believing it is real. This meditation allows one to connect with the true "I" that contains infinite wisdom and is full of endless possibility and potential.

Intention

To quiet the thinking mind and recognize that you are all things

Instructions

1. Sit up tall with your spine straight, eyes closed, and palms face up in your lap.
2. Bring your attention to your breath.
3. Say "sooooo" to yourself silently for the length of the inhale.
4. Say "hummm" to yourself silently for the duration of the exhale.
5. Once in the mantra, begin to expand your awareness outside of your body as you continue the mantra.
6. When a thought arises, simply return your attention to the mantra "so hum."

*KIRTAN KRIYA

Time: 12 min

Background

Kirtan Kriya is a type of meditation from Kundalini yoga, which has been practiced for thousands of years. A preliminary study investigated the results of a Kirtan Kriya meditation program performed for 12 minutes a day with adults ages 52–70 with MCI or complaints of memory difficulties. This group was compared to participants in a music group. Mini-Mental State Examination scores of the participants ranged from 24–30. After 8 weeks, the meditation group resulted in a statistically significant improvement in verbal fluency testing compared to the music group. The meditation group also showed increased performance in several other neuropsychological tests including the Trail Making Test B, and the Wechsler Adult Intelligence Scale (WAIS) Digit Symbol Substitution Test and Logical Memory Delayed test.

Intention

To improve cognitive-linguistic skills by retraining the brain to reduce stress

Instructions

1. While sitting with a straight spine and eyes closed, repeat the mantra "Sa, Ta, Na, Ma" with your hands in your lap, using the finger positions illustrated below.
   a. Sa: Touch index fingers to thumbs
   b. Ta: Touch middle fingers to thumbs
   c. Na: Touch ring fingers to thumbs
   d. Ma: Touch little fingers to thumbs
2. Sing the mantra in a normal voice (2 minutes).
3. Sing the mantra in a whisper voice (2 minutes).

4. Say the mantra silently to yourself (4 minutes).

5. Reverse: whisper (2 minutes), normal voice (2 minutes).

6. Inhale deeply, stretch your arms above your head, and sweep them down slowly on the exhale.

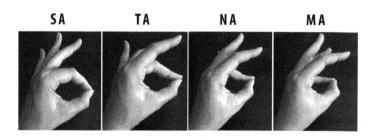

OPEN FOCUS

What is Open Focus? Dr. Les Fehmi is one of the world's leaders in neurofeedback and co-author of *The Open-Focus Brain*. The purpose of neurofeedback is to train the brain to operate in coherence so that the left and right brain are working together in a relaxed yet focused state. Paying attention in a narrow and fixated way (like we were trained to do in school) puts the brain on "high alert," creating increased stress. Open-Focus attention (being aware of the space in and around objects) produces the alpha brain wave states we experience when we are relaxed and in the zone.

Open Focus may feel unnatural at first because we have been culturally conditioned to "zoom in," be *faster*, get *more* done, etc. But it absolutely works.

Being in Open Focus is exactly the feeling we get when we are *in the zone*. We are relaxed and focused at the same time. Essentially, our senses are open, instead of being narrowly fixated on a single point of interest.

Note: It is more important that we are feeling the space or sensing it with our bodies than just visualizing or seeing it with our eyes. Open Focus is not an intellectual process but rather a feeling process using "space" (i.e., being "no thing"). This helps us to get beyond the busy left brain to a state where the left and right brain are working together, sending the body into a feeling state of homeostasis.

SPACE IN THE ROOM

Time: 5 min

Background

The more we focus on our physical bodies (i.e., I'm in pain!), the more we drain our energy resources that can be used for healing. By opening our focus in a slow but expansive way, we can begin to imagine the space in and around our bodies. This allows us to relax the brain and body and induce coherent brain wave states associated with higher levels of performance.

Intention

To induce a relaxed but focused state for an optimum level of performance in any activity

Instructions

Ask yourself or your patient the following questions, pausing for about 15 seconds in between each one. Remember, the exercise is about feeling the silence or space to which the question points, as opposed to answering the question in an intellectual or visual way.

1. Can I feel the space in my body?
2. Can I imagine the space that my body takes up in this room?
3. Can I imagine the space that this room takes up on this floor?
4. Can I imagine the space that this floor takes up in this building?
5. Can I imagine the space that this building takes up on this street?
6. Can I imagine the space that this street takes up in this city?
7. Can I imagine the space that this city takes up in this state?
8. Can I imagine the space that this state takes up in this country?
9. Can I imagine the space that this country takes up on Earth?

10. Can I imagine the space that the earth takes up in the entire universe?

11. Can I imagine the space that my body takes up in the entire universe?

Note: While Open-Focus exercises can be done independently, recording the questions and/ or having someone read them to you while your eyes are closed can enhance the process by eliminating visual stimulation.

SPACE IN & AROUND THE BODY

Time: 5 min

Background

As discussed, everything physical is made of atoms, which primarily consist of empty space or energy. Narrow-focus attention drains energy; Open-Focus attention, sensing the space or energy both in and around objects (including our bodies), literally grants us access to a greater field of energy that has been scientifically shown to facilitate healing. One of Dr. Joe Dispenza's most popular products, the meditation CD *Blessing of the Energy Centers*, explains the value of this practice in much greater detail.

Intention

To induce relaxation and focus by connecting to the energy field in the body

Instructions

Give yourself or your patient the following instructions, pausing for about 15 seconds in between each one. Remember, the exercise is about feeling energy or space, as opposed to thinking about the instructions in an intellectual or visual way.

1. Feel the energy or space in my hands.
2. Feel the energy or space in my feet.
3. Feel the energy or space in my elbows.
4. Feel the energy or space around my elbows.
5. Feel the energy or space in my knees.
6. Feel the energy or space in the entire length of my arms.
7. Feel the energy or space in the entire length of my legs.
8. Feel the energy or space right below my belly button.

9. Feel the energy or space around my belly button.

10. Feel the energy or space in my heart.

11. Feel the energy or space around my heart.

12. Feel the energy or space in my throat.

13. Feel the energy or space around my throat.

14. Feel the energy or space in my head.

15. Feel the energy or space around my head.

16. Feel the energy or space of my entire body.

17. Feel the energy or space that is around my body.

Note: While Open-Focus exercises can be done independently, recording the instructions and/or having someone read them to you while your eyes are closed can enhance the process by eliminating visual stimulation.

HEALING MEDITATIONS

OPENING OF THE CHAKRAS

Table 3. Chakra Colors, Locations, And Emotions

Chakra	Associated Color	Location	Emotions
Root	Red	Base of the spine	Basic needs such as food and money
Sacral	Orange	Lower abdomen ≈ 2 inches below navel	Connection and creation (abundance, well-being, pleasure)
Solar Plexus	Yellow	Upper abdomen	Personal power and self-worth
Heart	Green	Center of the chest	Love, joy, and inner peace
Throat	Blue	Throat	Communication and self-expression
Third Eye	Blue-Purple	Between the eyebrows	Intuition, imagination, inner wisdom
Crown	Purple	Top of the head	Connection to the Divine

Time: 10 min

Background

Chakras come from the Hindu tradition. They are discussed in several alternative wellness practices including yoga and Reiki. Chakras are energy centers in the body, and the seven major energy centers are listed in Table 3. Each are associated with a location in the body, a color, and emotions.

Intention

To clear stagnant energy and bring healing energy to our chakras

Instructions

1. Sit in a chair with feet flat on the floor, or sit on the floor with legs crossed.
2. Begin to feel the ground and imagine that you are connected with the earth.
3. Start with the Root chakra and imagine the base of your spine as a rotating red beam of energy. Spend 1–2 minutes in this space, allowing it to release old or blocked energy, making room for positive energy and healing.
4. Repeat for each chakra in the order listed on Table 3 until you reach the Crown.
5. Imagine a line connecting all seven chakras. Then, visualize a green healing light around your entire body.

CREATE YOUR OWN HEALING

Time: 5 min

Background

Mantra comes from the Sanskrit word meaning "instrument of thought." A mantra is a sound, word, or sentence repeated during meditation to focus the mind.

Intention

To create whatever you desire

Instructions

1.   Choose an area of your life or a part of your body that you wish to heal.

2.   Create a mantra. Below are some examples.

>   I am well.

>   I am healthy and joyful.

>   I expand in abundance.

>   I am perfection.

3.   Choose a position.

>   Sitting in a chair with eyes closed

>   Siting on the floor with eyes closed

>   Walking with eyes open

>   Lying down with arms 6–8 inches from your side and palms facing up

4.   Choose your breath work.

>   Focusing on your natural breath

>   Doubling the exhale

>   Lengthening the breath

5.   Follow your meditation as long as you feel is necessary to achieve your desired result.

REFERENCES & RECOMMENDED RESOURCES

Alexander, C. N., Langer, E. J., Newman, R. I., Chandler, H. M., & Davies, J. L. (1989). Transcendental meditation, mindfulness, and longevity: an experimental study with the elderly. *Journal of personality and social psychology, 57*(6), 950.

Brach, T. (2003). *Radical acceptance: Embracing your life with the heart of a Buddha.* New York, NY: Bantam Dell.

Childre, D., Martin, H., & Beech, D. (1999). *The HeartMath solution: The Heartmath Institute's revolutionary program for engaging the power of the heart's intelligence.* New York, NY: HarperOne.

Chopra, D. (2010, October 25). Mind body medicine: Your mind as a gateway to better health. [Web log post] Retrieved from http://www.huffingtonpost.com/deepak-chopra/your-mind-as-a-gateway-to_b_772981.html

DartingtonTV (2011, June 20). *Deepak Chopra: Physical healing, emotional wellbeing.* [Video file] Retrieved from https://www.youtube.com/watch?v=_gJN7I0a9XU

Dispenza, J. (2014). *You are the placebo: Making your mind matter.* Carlsbad, CA: Hay House, Inc.

Fehmi, L., & Robbins, J. (2008). *The open-focus brain: Harnessing the power of attention to heal mind and body.* Boston, MA: Trumpeter.

Hölzel, B. K., Carmody, J., Vangel, M., Congleton, C., Yerramsetti, S. M., Gard, T., & Lazar, S.W. (2011). Mindfulness practice leads to increases in regional brain gray matter density. *Psychiatry Research: Neuroimaging, 191*(1), 36–43. http://dx.doi.org/10.1016/j.pscychresns.2010.08.006

Luders, E., Kurth, F., Mayer, E. A., Toga, A. W., Narr, K. L., & Gaser, C. (2012). The unique brain anatomy of meditation practitioners: alterations in cortical gyrification. *Frontiers in Human Neuroscience, 6*(34). http://dx.doi.org/10.3389/fnhum.2012.00034

Marciniak, R., Sheardova, K., Čermáková, P., Hudeček, D., Šumec, R., & Hort, J. (2014). Effect of meditation on cognitive functions in context of aging and neurodegenerative diseases. *Frontiers in Behavioral Neuroscience, 8*(17). http://doi.org/10.3389/fnbeh.2014.00017

Marshall, R. S., Basilakos, A., Williams, T., & Love-Myers, K. (2014). Exploring the benefits of unilateral nostril breathing practice post-stroke: Attention, language, spatial abilities, depression, and anxiety. *Journal of Alternative and Complementary Medicine, 20*(3), 185194. DOI:10.1089/acm.2013.0019

Marshall, R. S., Laures-Gore, J., DuBay, M., Williams, T., & Bryant, D. (2015). Unilateral Forced Nostril Breathing and Aphasia— Exploring Unilateral Forced Nostril Breathing as an Adjunct to Aphasia Treatment: A Case Series. *The Journal of Alternative and Complementary Medicine, 21*(2), 91–99.

Mitchell, A. J., & Shiri-Feshki, M. (2009). Rate of progression of mild cognitive impairment to dementia—meta-analysis of 41 robust inception cohort studies. *Acta Psychiatrica Scandinavica, 119*(4), 252–265. DOI:10.1111/j.1600-0447.2008.01326.x

Mortimer, J. A., Ding, D., Borenstein, A.R., DeCarli, C., Guo, Q., Wu, Y., Zhao, Q., & Chu, S. (2012). Changes in brain volume and cognition in a randomized trial of exercise and social interaction in a community-based sample of non-demented Chinese elders. *Journal of Alzheimer's Disease, 30*(4), 757–766. DOI: 10.3233/JAD-2012-120079

Newberg, A. B., Wintering, N., Khalsa, D. S., Roggenkamp, H., & Waldman, M. R. (2010). Meditation effects on cognitive function and cerebral blood flow in subjects with memory loss: A preliminary study. *Journal of Alzheimer's Disease, 20*(2), 517526. DOI: 10.3233/JAD-2010-1391

Newberg, A. B., Wintering, N., Waldman, M. R., Amen, D., Khalsa, D. S., & Alavi, A. (2010). Cerebral blood flow differences between long-term meditators and non-meditators. *Consciousness and Cognition, 19*(4), 899–905. http://dx.doi.org/10.1016/j.concog.2010.05.003

Prakash, R., Rastogi, P., Dubey, I., Abhishek, P., Chaudhury, S., & Small, B. J. (2012). Long-term concentrative meditation and cognitive performance among older adults. *Aging, Neuropsychology, and Cognition, 19*(4), 479–494.

Shimoff, M., Kline, C. (2010). *Love for no reason: 7 steps for creating a life of unconditional love.* New York, NY: Atria.

Tolle, E. (1999). *The power of now: A guide to spiritual enlightenment.* Novato, CA: New World Library.

Wilson, R. S., Schneider, J. A., Boyle, P. A., Arnold, S. E., Tang, Y., & Bennett, D. A. (2007). Chronic distress and incidence of mild cognitive impairment. *Neurology, 68*(24), 2085–2092. http://dx.doi.org/10.1212/01.wnl.0000264930.97061.82

Zeidan, F., Johnson, S. K., Diamond, B. J., David, Z., & Goolkasian, P. (2010). Mindfulness meditation improves cognition: Evidence of brief mental training. *Consciousness and Cognition, 19*(2), 597–605 http://dx.doi.org/10.1016/j.concog.2010.03.014

For more information on Dr. Joe Dispenza's work, please visit: drjoedispenza.com.

For more information on Dr. Les Fehmi's work, please visit: openfocus.com.

ACKNOWLEDGEMENTS

From Jennifer—

First, I would like to thank my spiritual partner Dan for tirelessly guiding my emotional intelligence and spiritual development over the last 11 years.

I would like to acknowledge my Mom and Dad. Thank you for fostering my creativity and wonder. I have always colored outside the lines because of your faith in my spirit.

And thank you to my husband, Ian. He has been a true model for seeing the best in every person and situation. Since day one, he has fearlessly encouraged me to dream bigger than I ever thought possible.

Finally, I would like to thank my newest spiritual teacher, Graycen. When you think you are enlightened, have a kid!

From Dan—

I would like to thank my spiritual partner Jen for embracing this journey with me and for the idea to write this book.

I would also like to acknowledge my boss Lila for allowing me the freedom to "field test" over the last ten years many of the ideas shared here.

To my friends and mentors Karin and Karl, thank you for being such amazing "Mindful Life" role models. Your unconditional guidance and support played a huge role in the creation of this book.

I am also so grateful for the countless teachers who have shared the wisdom of their experiences to make it easier for others. Eckhart

Tolle, Tara Brach, Dr. Joe Dispenza, and Dr. Les Fehmi are at the top of my list.

Finally, I would like to thank "life" itself. You, through my favorite activities (e.g., poker & golf), tirelessly teach me how I can always be a better role model for what I am teaching.

ABOUT THE AUTHORS

DAN EISNER, MS, OTR/L, CC

Dan is a psychiatric Occupational Therapist at the University of Maryland Medical Center and a private certified coach at www. DanEisnerConsulting.com with over 18 years of experience. Dan has been inspiring thousands of people with his unique blend of services based on the latest advances in neuroscience and practical spirituality. He passionately believes that everyone already has their own answers but understands that most people are too stressed and distracted to access their own wisdom on a regular basis. By teaching the practical applications of how to stay clear and focused, Dan provides each patient with a "road map" that explains the behavior, thereby making it easier to change. Dan's ultimate mission is to inspire others to trust their intuition and to stay on their own path.

JENNIFER LLADO, MS, MS, CCC-SLP

Jennifer is the founder of Bright Side Therapy, LLC, which produces innovative therapy materials for speech-language pathologists. She is a practicing speech-language pathologist with over 10 years of experience in various healthcare settings. Jennifer has an additional master's degree in leadership and a graduate certificate in health management. In 2012, Jennifer was part of the first American Speech-Language-Hearing Association's Leadership Development Program. She is also a certified clinical aromatherapist and a certified Reiki practitioner and currently works as a director of rehabilitation across two hospital sites. Jennifer is passionate about meditation and alternative healthcare practices and is dedicated to bringing consciousness to healthcare and leadership.

The Backstory

Dan and Jen met during Jen's SLP internship in Baltimore, in 2005. Over the last decade, they have cultivated a spiritual partnership. Author Gary Zukov defines a spiritual partnership as "a relationship between equals for the purpose of spiritual growth." Gradually, they learned about meditation and the power of thought and shared honest feedback with one another for the purpose of becoming better people and healthcare practitioners.

And together, they created the idea of . . .

Mindful Healthcare

Mindful Healthcare is dedicated to training clinicians and patients to access their highest level of performance. It inspires the very best in both patients and practitioners by offering a pragmatic approach for optimizing the ability to focus and to maintain a balanced energy. Do you want to be "in the zone" on a more regular basis? Then please join us in becoming self-aware, visionary leaders by making Mindful Healthcare an integral part of your practice.

Contact us for more information on Mindful Healthcare training:

dan@daneisnerconsulting.com

www.daneisnerconsulting.com

Subscribe to our list:

www.daneisnerconsulting.com

Follow our blog:

http://www.daneisnerconsulting.com/blog

Join us on Facebook:

https://www.facebook.com/mindfulhealthcaring/

Dear Valued Reader,

Dan Eisner Consulting & Bright Side Therapy, LLC are committed to producing innovative, up-to-date, and age-appropriate treatment tools. In order to continue making high-quality products, we are requesting your honest feedback. Please feel free to email your comments or thoughts to dan@daneisnerconsulting.com or jen@brightsidetherapy.com.

We look forward to hearing from you!

Sincerely,

Dan Eisner & Jennifer Llado

"Logic will get you from A to B.
Imagination will take you everywhere."
–Albert Einstein

61691921R00034

Made in the USA
Lexington, KY
17 March 2017